This book belongs to

If pirates lived a life of kindness,
maybe they would find,
that not all problems call for violence,
and love is never blind.

Welcome to my illustrated world of Pirates!

Relax and explore a world of beautifully detailed pen–and–ink illustrations – all waiting to be brought to life through color. For artists and seafarers of all ages.

The artworks in my books are based on illustrations I have drawn over my years as an artist. The designs are filled with imaginative detail whilst remaining fun and accessible to younger colorists.

The illustrations come with some pirate themed poetry, for your enjoyment and to help set the mood.

See more at rjhampson.com

 russelljamesart

Published by Hop Skip Jump
PO Box 1324 Buderim Queensland Australia 4556

First published 2020.
Copyright © 2023 R.J. Hampson.

ISBN: 978-1-922472-28-1

Using this book

Find a quiet place away from distractions. Relax and immerse yourself in the process of coloring as you explore the details of each fantastic illustration.

This book is best suited to color pencils or markers. Wet mediums should be used sparingly. Slide a card behind the illustration you are coloring to avoid marker bleed through.

Find fresh coloring pages by signing up to the R.J. Hampson newsletter. Get free downloadable pages and updates on new books at -

rjhampson.com/coloring

Hidden

A lifetime wasted filling up a purse. Laughing at the rumors of a curse.
But when the truth is told, your soul will shrink with cold.
There's no warmth in all the money that you nurse.

The Harrowing Incident of the Hot Chip by the Seaside

A flock of birds hovering above, they want my chips; they have no love.

Trust Me, I'm a Pirate

We took an oath; we swore to keep, upon a desert isle.
But I'll be back, all on my own, in just a little while.

Pipe Dreams

Do pirates dream of what they've seen? How will we ever know?
Of spinning tales they're over keen–but I'd not tell them so.

The Hunter

If you're searching for a whale, don't use a little boat.
For if you find the thing you hunt, you'll really need to float.

The Kraken

Release the kraken, someone said, and Larry pulled the lever.
None of us were seen again, not now, not then, not ever.

Row Boat

Yesterday I had a bigger boat. It kept a rowdy company afloat.
But drinking too much rum has made me come undone,
and now there's only me upon the sea.

The Pirate and the Persimmon Tree

Not all treasure hides inside a chest.
Forbidden fruit is oftentimes the best.

Where?

I hid my treasure in a hole, it's full of lovely things I stole.
Too many knocks upon my noggin, I need a map for gains ill-gotten.

A New Boat

A new boat for me. A new boat for free.
And anyone complaining, was thrown into the sea.

Sinking

The fickle hand of fate has made its final tricky stand,
and thrown me from my favorite boat a long, long way from land.

Three Men in a Boat

Three pirate captains went to sea, but none of them would row.
How long this stand-off lasted, we'll never ever know.

Space Pirates

Would pirates in a vacuum ever miss the breeze?
And what would happen if they had to sneeze?

Lullaby

When pirates sing a lullaby who is it that is sleepy?
For we all know that pirate songs can be a little weepy.
So if you're in the deep blue sea and hear a gentle song,
be sure to batten down your hatch in case they come along.

Pirates Peril

A pirate's life is not a piece of cake.
He does not sail his boat upon a lake.

Retirement

Old pirates never die. They're soaked in rum, don't wonder why.
They live in breezy villas, and feast on seagull pie.

Pirate Love

A pirate's love is fickle like the sea. A harsher mistress there could never be.
If you hug a pirate to your breast, know he'll be thinking of his treasure chest.

Big

The sea was big that day my friend, but none of us were daunted.
That's why the ocean waves are now most definitely haunted.

Pirates Lair

If you see a pirate's lair, make sure you do not stop to stare.
For pirates know, and pirates care, and pirates are not fair.

Blue Beard

Cut your beard, you scurvy dog, before you disappear.
You look a bit too furry to fill your foes with fear.

Bird Cage

All albatross and pirates should be friends.
They both traverse the waters hand in hand.
Their friendship is well noted, it seems to last the age.
So why are pirates dreaming of a cage?

Lookout

The fairest pirate of them all was blest with eagle's eye.
She watched the far horizons from her crow's nest up on high.

Narwhal

Pirates riding whales could tell a ripping yarn and then,
dive deep beneath the roiling swell to not be seen again.

The Lookout Bar

Come slake your thirst at the Lookout Bar.
If you have a boat, it's not too far.

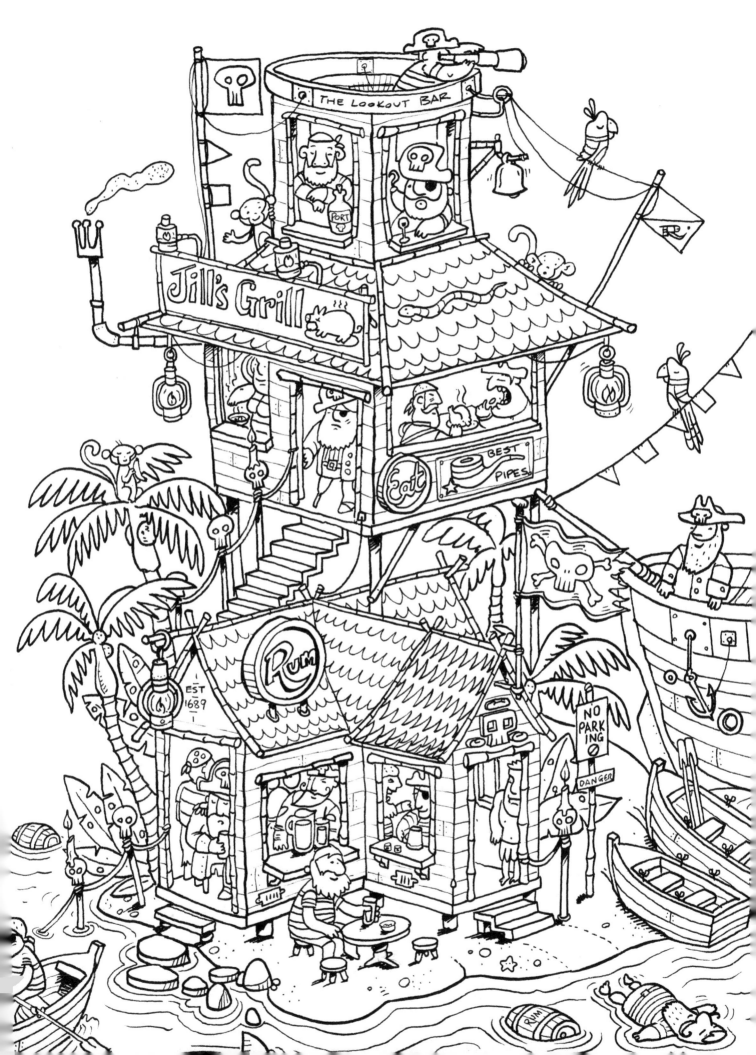

Aargh, There be a battle ahead – Beware!

Find more treasure!

Find new coloring pages by signing up to Russell's newsletter.
Get free downloadable pages and updates on new books at -
rjhampson.com/coloring

Thanks for choosing this coloring book.
If you enjoyed it, please consider leaving a review.
It will help to let more people in on the experience
plus you'd certainly make this illustrator very happy!

Published books in this series

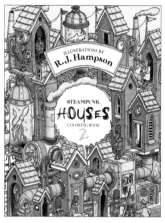

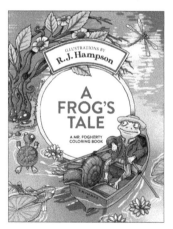

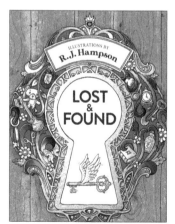

See flip-throughs and new releases at **rjhampson.com**